11+
Verbal Reasoning
GL & Other Styles

WORKBOOK 2

Verbal Reasoning Technique

Dr Stephen C Curran

Edited by Jacqui Turner & Andrea Richardson

This book belongs to

Accelerated Education Publications Ltd

Contents

Chapter Five
LOGICAL REASONING

Logical Reasoning questions are of three types:

Tabular • **Relational** • **Positional**

1. Tabular Reasoning

These questions involve the processing of a large amount of information and are solved by creating a grid or table.

Example: Andy, Bharat, Chris, Danielle and Edward all collect things. Andy, Bharat and Chris each collect stamps. Danielle collects cards, games and stamps. Andy collects stickers. Edward collects coins and stickers. Bharat collects cards, games and coins.
a) Who collects the most things?
b) Who collects the least things?
c) Which child does not collect cards or stamps?

Set out the information on a grid like this. Make sure you have noted all the information from each of the statements.

	Stamps	Cards	Games	Stickers	Coins
A	✓	✗	✗	✓	✗
B	✓	✓	✓	✗	✓
C	✓	✗	✗	✗	✗
D	✓	✓	✓	✗	✗
E	✗	✗	✗	✓	✓

Answers from the grid or table:
a) Bharat collects the most things. b) Chris collects the least things. c) Edward does not collect cards or stamps.

Exercise 5: 1a   Answer the following:

1) William and Xu-min like Maths. William and Alex like English. Alex and Hyan like History. Hyan and Xu-min like Science.

Complete the table from the above statements before answering the questions below:

	Maths	English	History	Science
A				
H				
X				
W				

a) Who likes Maths and Science? _____

b) Who likes English and History? _____

2) Kim and Ronan are on the rowing team. Andrew and Michael play tennis. Fleur and Louise go horse riding. Ronan and Michael play lacrosse. Michael and Louise play hockey.

	Rowing	Tennis	Horse	Lacrosse	Hockey
A					
F					
K					
L					
R					
M					

a) Who goes horse riding and plays hockey? _____

b) Who plays the most sports? _____

3) Rupa, Rebecca, Ruth, Laura, Alice, Marion and Juliet play musical instruments. Rebecca, Marion and Juliet play the violin. Ruth plays the double bass. Alice and Laura are learning the clarinet. They all play the piano.

	Violin	D-Bass	Clarinet	Piano
A				
J				
L				
M				
Re				
Rup				
Rut				

Complete the table from the above statements before answering the questions below.

Take care as this table is more complex. It requires accuracy when filling it in and careful observation when reading it.

a) Who plays the double bass and the piano? _____

b) Who plays only one instrument? _____

4) Ray likes biscuits and cakes. David enjoys chocolate. Jasper prefers biscuits and toffee. Claire likes chocolate but does not like cakes. All the boys like fudge.

	Bisc	Cakes	Choc	Toffee	Fudge
R					
D					
J					
C					

Which two children like three types of sweet?

A. Ray and Jasper   B. Claire and Ray

C. Jasper and David   D. David and Claire

Some questions require a much simpler grid, but it is still worth organising your ideas to avoid a mistake.

Example:

> A cat has five kittens. Two are tabby and two are white. All white and tortoiseshell kittens have green eyes. The white kittens are male. The black kittens have blue eyes.

1. Place each item of information on a table using abbreviations.
2. Irrelevant information is often included in the question.
3. Nothing is known about the fifth kitten. It may be any of the four colours. The last statement about black kittens having blue eyes is irrelevant.

	Col	Eyes	M/F
1	Ta		
2	Ta		
3	W	G	M
4	W	G	M
5			

The completely true statement must then be selected.

A. None of the kittens is tortoiseshell. **Unknown.**
B. None of the kittens has blue eyes. **Unknown.**
C. The tabby kittens have brown eyes. **Unknown.**
D. All of the kittens are female. **False.**
E. **At least two of the kittens have green eyes. True.**

Exercise 5: 1b Answer the following:

5) Callum, Zara, Joshua and Mary like reading. Joshua and Mary like non-fiction books while Callum and Zara prefer fiction. Zara and Mary like books about horses while Callum and Joshua prefer books about machines.

Complete the table from the above statements before answering the questions below:

	Type	About
C	F	M
J	N-F	
M		
Z		

Are the following statements **True**, **False** or **Unknown**?

A. Callum likes non-fiction books about machines. _____

B. Mary's favourite author is Nicolas Evans. _____

C. Zara likes fictional books about horses. _____

6) Some children had a meal at a food hall. Phillip and Daniel ate sushi. Ben and Anna ate pizza. Olivia and Ryan ate kebabs. Phillip and Ben drank coffee. Daniel, Olivia and Ryan drank orange juice. Anna drank lemonade.

	Ate	Drank
A		
B		
D		
O		
P		
R		

Are the following statements **True** or **False**?

A. Phillip drank orange juice with his sushi. _____

B. Olivia ate pizza. _____

C. Ryan drank orange juice with his kebab. _____

7) Jill, Rae, Ada, Jan, Tim and Eva like cooking. Jan and Rae like making cakes. Rae, Ada, Jan and Tim like cooking pasta. Jill and Eva like cooking bread.

	Cake	Pasta	Bread
Jill			
Rae			
Ada			
Jan			
Tim			
Eva			

Are the following statements **True**, **False** or **Unknown**?

A. Jill does not like cooking apple pie. _____

B. Jill likes cooking bread and cakes. _____

C. Ada likes cooking pasta and bread. _____

2. Relational Reasoning

Relational Reasoning questions appear in two forms:

Relative Information • **Relative Meaning**

A. Relative Information - This type involves sorting out and reordering statements that relate to each other.

Example:

Train 1 leaves the Railway Station at 9.00am. Train 2 leaves at 8.45am. Train 2 takes twice as long as Train 3 to make the same journey. Train 3 leaves 15 minutes after Train 1 and arrives at 10.00am.

What time does Train 2 arrive?

A. 9.45am	B. 9.30am
C. 10.00am	D. 10.15am

It is important to understand each statement precisely and how it relates to the other statements. Reordering the statements will help unravel the information.

We need to find out about Train 2. This is done by seeing how the timings for Train 2 relate to the other trains. The information can be summarised as follows:

1. Train 2 takes twice as long as Train 3.

2. Train 3 leaves 15 minutes after Train 1, which means it leaves at 9.15am. (Train 1 leaves at 9.00am.) It arrives at 10.00am. It takes 45 minutes.

3. Train 2 takes twice as long, so it takes 90 minutes to complete the journey.

Putting the information onto a chart can help. This can be done in a number of ways but below is a suggestion.

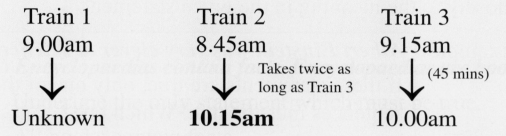

Train 1	Train 2	Train 3
9.00am	8.45am	9.15am
	Takes twice as long as Train 3	(45 mins)
↓	↓	↓
Unknown	**10.15am**	10.00am

Train 2 left at 8.45am. The 90 minute journey means it arrived at 10.15am. Therefore the answer is D.

Exercise 5: 1c Answer the following:

8) a) At an airport some flights were due to arrive. Flight AE001 was due in 10 minutes. Flight AE002 was due in 20 minutes but was running 20 minutes late.

Are the following statements **True**, **False** or **Unknown**?

A. Flight AE001 was flying in from Dubai. _____

B. Flight AE002 was due to land after AE001. _____

C. Flight AE002 was due to arrive at 6.40pm. _____

b) Isabella, Amy, Rowan and Peter went to a tuition centre. Isabella and Rowan always complete their homework. Amy completes most of her homework. Peter rarely completes his homework.

Are the following statements **True**, **False** or **Unknown**?

A. Rowan completed his homework last week. _____

B. Isabella spends more time on homework than Amy. _____

C. Isabella never completes her homework. _____

B. Relative Meaning - Some questions involve selecting a statement from the possible answers that relates most closely to the meaning in the given statement.

Example:

> *Albert Einstein was very clever at science.*
>
> If these statements are true, only one of the sentences must be true. Which one?
>
> A. Science was invented by Albert Einstein.
> B. Albert Einstein really enjoyed doing science.
> C. Albert Einstein was a scientist.
> D. Science is always done by clever scientists.

Some possible answers may be true in themselves, but the correct answer must match the meaning of the given statement precisely and not add or detract from it.

Answer A - 'Science was invented by Albert Einstein.' This does not line up with the statement and is not true anyway.

Answer B - 'Albert Einstein really enjoyed doing science.' We are given no specific information about Albert Einstein's attitude to science.

Answer D - 'Science is always done by clever scientists.'
It is not relevant to the statement and is not necessarily true.

Answer C - **'Albert Einstein was a scientist.'**

This is the only answer that correctly matches the given statement in all respects. It follows that if *'Albert Einstein was very clever at science'*, he can be correctly called a scientist.

Exercise 5: 1d Answer the following:

9) a) ***London is in England. London is a city.***

Underline the only statement which must be true.

England is a city.
London is an English city.
London is a city because it is in England.

b) ***Oranges are citrus fruits. Oranges grow on trees.***

Underline the only statement which must be true.

All fruit on trees is citrus fruit.
Oranges are the only citrus fruit.
Oranges grow on citrus fruit trees.
All citrus fruits are orange in colour.

10) a) ***Pandas are bears. Pandas are black and white.***

Underline the only statement which must be true.

All bears are black and white.
Bears come in many colours.
White bears are always pandas.
Pandas are black and white bears.

b) *Crocodiles are predators. Crocodiles wait for their prey under water.*

Underline the only statement which must be true.

Crocodiles attack their prey from the water.
Crocodiles wait for their prey on land.
Crocodiles eat all animals.
Other animals eat crocodiles.

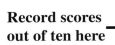 Record scores out of ten here →

3. Positional Reasoning

Positional Reasoning questions appear in many forms. They can relate to **Age**, **Time**, **Direction**, **Size** and **Order**.

All positional reasoning questions are best solved with **diagrams**. This allows precise organisation of the given information and avoids confusion.

a. Basic Types

Most positional reasoning questions are straightforward and can be solved with a simple diagram.

Example:

Peter lives one floor above Terry and one floor below Yvonne. Derek lives two floors above Terry.

Which two people live on the same floor?
 A. Yvonne and Terry
 B. Peter and Derek
 C. Peter and Terry
 D. Derek and Terry
 E. Yvonne and Derek

Draw a grid that represents the floors of the block and, with trial and error, plot the position of each person.

3	Y D
2	P
1	T

Eventually it will be seen there is only one possible combination that will fit all the requirements.

Answer: E. **Yvonne and Derek** live on the same floor.

Exercise 5: 2a   Answer the following:

1) Penny is taller than Gary. Matthew is shorter than Gary but taller than Rebecca.   _____

(Use these lines to plot their positions.)   _____

_____

_____

Underline the answers. Are they **True**, **False** or **Unknown**?

A. Penny is the tallest. (True, False or Unknown)

B. Matthew is the second tallest. (True, False or Unknown)

C. Gary would like to be taller than Penny.
   (True, False or Unknown)

_____

2) Four children run a race. Sonja runs faster than Rose. Rose is ten seconds faster than Sam. Kathy runs the fastest.

(Use the lines below to plot their positions.)

_____   _____   _____   _____

Underline the answers. Are they **True**, **False** or **Unknown**?

A. Rose is the second fastest. (True, False, Unknown)

B. Kathy trains every week. (True, False, Unknown)

C. Sam came last. (True, False, Unknown)

3) Chizu speaks more languages than Nadia. Alicia speaks more languages than Nadia but less than Chizu. Thalara speaks only one language.

(Use the lines below to plot their positions.)

_____   _____   _____   _____

Underline the answers. Are they **True** or **False**?

A. Chizu speaks the least number of languages.
   (True or False)
B. Nadia speaks the most languages. (True or False)
C. Alicia speaks the second highest number of languages.
   (True or False)

---

4) Five vehicles are waiting for the traffic lights to turn green. A blue car is positioned between a bus and a motorbike. A truck is behind the motorbike. A red car is positioned in front of the bus.

_____

_____   (Use these lines to plot
                        their positions.)
_____

_____

_____

Write whether the statements are **True**, **False** or **Unknown**?

A. The bus is closest to the traffic lights. _____
B. The blue car is closest to the traffic lights. _____
C. The bus is heading to Oxford. _____

b. Complex Types

Some positional reasoning questions are more **Complex**. They can still be solved with a diagrammatic approach, but it may not be quite so obvious which one to use.

Example:

> Rachel, Michael, Zarah and Freddie are 9, 8, 8 and 7 years old, but not in this order. Two of the children are twins. Rachel is one year younger than Zarah. Michael is one year younger than Freddie. Michael is older than Rachel.
>
> Which two children are twins?
>
> A. Freddie and Zarah   B. Freddie and Rachel
> C. Zarah and Michael   D. Rachel and Zarah
> E. Freddie and Michael

The information can be summarised as follows:

1. The four children are 9, 8, 8 and 7 years old. The twins must be 8 years old. There is only a two year gap in age between all the children.

2. Rachel is one year younger than Zarah.

3. Michael is one year younger than Freddie.

4. Michael is older than Rachel.

The statements must fit the pattern of the ages. Set out the ages and then try and fit the children into them.

The information provided in the first three statements only permits two possibilities as there are one year gaps in age between Zarah and Freddie and between Rachel and Michael.

Both possibilities are tested below in the age structure:

1st Possibility   (9)   Zarah

                 (8)   Rachel   (8)   Freddie

                 (7)   Michael

This is not the correct combination since the question states Michael is older than Rachel (see statement 4).

2nd Possibility   (9)   Freddie

                 (8)   **Zarah**   (8)   **Michael**

                 (7)   Rachel

The only possible combination is:

C. **Zarah and Michael are twins.**

Exercise 5: 2b   Answer the following:

5) a) Cameron is one year older than Jake who is three
     years older than Sophie. Sophie is eight.

      _____

      _____   (Use the diagram
                        to help you.)

      _____

     Underline the only statement that must be true.

     A. Jake is 9.

     B. Cameron is younger than Sophie.

     C. Cameron is 12.

---

   b) If the day before yesterday was a Friday,
      what day will it be the day after tomorrow? _____

                              Today

(Use this diagram to help you.) _____ _____ _____ _____ _____

4. Mixed Examples

Exercise 5: 2c Answer the following:

6) Matthew, Mark, John and James keep fish as pets. Matthew and Mark have goldfish. John and James have clown fish. Matthew and James keep their fish in a bowl while Mark and John keep their fish in ponds.

Underline the answers. Are they **True**, **False** or **Unknown**?

A. Matthew keeps goldfish in a pond. (True, False, Unknown)
B. James has more fish than Mark. (True, False, Unknown)
C. John keeps clown fish in a bowl. (True, False, Unknown)
D. James keeps clown fish in a bowl. (True, False, Unknown)

---

7) a) *Encyclopaedias contain facts. Encyclopaedias are books.*

Underline the only statement which must be true.

All books contain facts.
All books are encyclopaedias.
Dictionaries are encyclopaedias.
Some books contain facts.
Encyclopaedias contain fiction.

b) *Castles are fortresses. Most castles have moats.*

Underline the only statement which must be true.

Moats are rarely found around castle fortresses.
Castles are fortresses that defend moats.
Moats surround many castle fortresses.
All castle fortresses have moats.
Moats are full of water.

8) The school record for a race was 45 seconds. Marion beat the school record by 5 seconds. Deborah took 8 seconds longer than Marion.

Underline the only statement that must be true.

A. Deborah took 53 seconds to run the race.
B. Marion took 50 seconds to run the race.
C. Deborah took 48 seconds to run the race.
D. Deborah took 47 seconds to run the race.

9) Joseph is three years older than Noah, who is two years older than Li. Li is seven.

How old is Joseph? (Underline the answer.)

A. Five years old
B. Two years old
C. Nine years old
D. Twelve years old

10) a) Tomorrow is Wednesday. What day of the week was it yesterday? (Underline the answer.)

A. Saturday
B. Sunday
C. Monday
D. Tuesday

b) If the day after tomorrow will be the 2nd of October, what was the date yesterday? (Underline the answer.)

A. The 30th of September
B. The 28th of September
C. The 29th of September
D. The 1st of October

Score

Chapter Six
MATHEMATICAL REASONING

There are four types of **Mathematical Reasoning** question:
Substitution • **Equation** • **Sequencing** • **Number Link**

1. Substitution

These questions employ a simple form of Algebra, where letters stand for numbers. **Substitute** the numbers for the letters and do the calculation (using $+ - \times \div$). When the answer is obtained it must be converted back to a letter.

Example:

> $A = 2, B = 3, C = 4, D = 10, E = 12$
> What is the answer to this sum written as a letter?

Substitute the numbers for the letters:

$A \times B + C$

$2 \times 3 + 4 = 10 \ (D)$

The answer is: **D**

Exercise 6: 1 Write the answer as a letter:

Score

1) $A = 2, B = 3, C = 4, D = 5, E = 6$
What is the answer to this sum written as a letter?

$A + B = \underline{\hspace{2cm}}$

2) **A = 1, B = 2, C = 3, D = 4, E = 8**
What is the answer to this sum written as a letter?

$$D - C = \underline{\qquad}$$

3) **A = 2, B = 12, C = 3, D = 6, E = 8**
What is the answer to this sum written as a letter?

$$A \times C = \underline{\qquad}$$

4) **A = 1, B = 2, C = 5, D = 6, E = 10**
What is the answer to this sum written as a letter?

$$E \div C = \underline{\qquad}$$

5) **A = 3, B = 4, C = 6, D = 7, E = 9**
What is the answer to this sum written as a letter?

$$E - C = \underline{\qquad}$$

6) **A = 2, B = 3, C = 4, D = 6, E = 8**
What is the answer to this sum written as a letter?

$$A \times B + A = \underline{\qquad}$$

7) **A = 1, B = 2, C = 5, D = 7, E = 10**
What is the answer to this sum written as a letter?

$$E \div C + C = \underline{\qquad}$$

8) **A = 1, B = 2, C = 3, D = 5, E = 6**
What is the answer to this sum written as a letter?

$$A \times B + C = \underline{\qquad}$$

9) **A = 2, B = 3, C = 4, D = 5, E = 10**

What is the answer to this sum written as a letter?

$$C \times A - B = \underline{\hspace{2cm}}$$

10) **A = 1, B = 2, C = 3, D = 5, E = 6**

What is the answer to this sum written as a letter?

$$E \div C + A = \underline{\hspace{2cm}}$$

2. Arithmetic Equations

It is important to understand the relationship between the Four Rules of Number. **Inverse** means **Opposite**.

+ and − are a pair of operations.

$$5 + 4 = \mathbf{9}; \qquad 9 - 4 = \mathbf{5}; \qquad 9 - 5 = \mathbf{4}$$

× and ÷ are a pair of operations.

$$3 \times 4 = \mathbf{12}; \qquad 12 \div 4 = \mathbf{3}; \qquad 12 \div 3 = \mathbf{4}$$

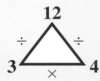

Equations are mathematical sentences. The numbers on the left side are **Balanced**, or **Equal**, to what is on the right side. This is signified by an **Equals Sign**.

The Equals Sign means a missing number can be found. **Inverse Operations** can be used to solve the equations.

Remember: + is **inverse to** − and × is **inverse to** ÷

Example: | Find the missing number in this equation:
$$8 \times 5 = 120 \div [?]$$

1. Multiply **8 × 5**

$$8 \times 5 = 120 \div [?]$$

2. To find the dividing number a division is necessary.

$$40 = 120 \div [?]$$

$$40 = 120 \div \boxed{3}$$

$$40 = 40$$

Divide **120 ÷ 40 = 3**

The answer is: **3**

Exercise 6: 2   Find the missing number:

1) **3 + 2 = 4 + [?]** ____

2) **8 − 1 = 2 + [?]** ____

3) **2 × 3 = 3 × [?]** ____

4) **17 − 2 = 5 + [?]** ____

5) **2 × 4 + 1 = 3 × [?]** ____

6) **8 ÷ 2 = 7 − [?]** ____

7) **17 + 2 = 25 − [?]** ____

8) **10 × 2 = 5 × [?]** ____

9) **9 − 6 = 3 × [?]** ____

10) **10 × 6 = 40 + [?]** ____

Score

3. Number Sequencing

The Four Rules of Number are the basis for all **Number Sequence** operations. $+ \ - \ \times \ \div$

Adding and **Subtracting** types could be called 'slow' sequences as the numbers get bigger or smaller slowly.

Multiplying and **Dividing** types could be called 'fast' sequences as the numbers get bigger or smaller quickly.

a. Adding and Subtracting

Basic Adding and Subtracting Sequences comprise:

1. Arithmetic Progressions
(Add/subtract a constant number)

$$\overset{+2}{3,} \ \overset{+2}{5,} \ \overset{+2}{7,} \ \overset{+2}{9,} \ \overset{+2}{11,} \ \overset{+2}{13,} \ ?$$

Example 1:

Add **2** to the previous number.

The next number will be: **15**

---

2. Increasing or Decreasing Gaps
(Add/subtract an increasing or decreasing number)

$$\overset{+1}{1,} \ \overset{+2}{2,} \ \overset{+3}{4,} \ \overset{+4}{7,} \ \overset{+5}{11,} \ \overset{+6}{16,} \ ?$$

Example 2:

Add **1**, then add **2**, then add **3**, etc.

The next number will be: **22**

---

3. Alternating Gaps
(Add/subtract numbers on an alternating basis)

$$\overset{+7}{1,} \ \overset{-3}{8,} \ \overset{+6}{5,} \ \overset{-4}{11,} \ \overset{+5}{7,} \ \overset{-5}{12,} \ ?$$

Example 3:

Add **7**, subtract **3**, add **6**, subtract **4**, etc.

The next number will be: **7**

Exercise 6: 3   Find the missing number:

1) **15, 13, 11, 9, 7,** ____

2) **18, 15, 12, 9, 6,** ____

3) **6, 11, 16, 21, 26,** ____

4) **2, 5, 8, 11, 14,** ____

5) **30, 25, 20, 15, 10,** ____

6) **5, 7, 10, 12, 15,** ____

7) **4, 6, 9, 11, 14,** ____

8) **3, 3, 4, 6, 9,** ____

9) **12, 11, 9, 8, 6,** ____

10) **2, 3, 2, 4, 3, 6 ,** ____

b. Multiplying and Dividing

Earlier features also apply to Multiply and Divide sequences.

Basic Multiplying and Dividing Sequences comprise:

1. **Multiply or Divide by the same number**
(Multiply/divide repeatedly)

Example 1:

Multiply by **2** on a repeated basis.

$\times 2 \quad \times 2 \quad \times 2 \quad \times 2 \quad \times 2 \quad \times 2$

1, 2, 4, 8, 16, 32, ?

The next number will be: **64**

This can also be seen as an arithmetic increasing gap sequence:

1, +1 **2,** +2 **4,** +4 **8,** +8 **16,** +16 **32,** +32 **64,** etc.

2. Geometric Progressions
(Multiply/divide repeatedly by an increasing number)

$\times 2$　$\times 3$　$\times 4$　$\times 5$　$\times 6$

1, 2, 6, 24, 120, ?

Example 2:

> Multiply by **2**, then by **3**, then by **4**, etc.

The next number will be: **720**

3a. Multiplying the Gaps
(Multiply/divide the gap by the same number)

(2×2)　(4×2)　(8×2)　(16×2)
　+2　　+4　　+8　　+16　　+32

0, 2, 6, 14, 30, ?

Example 3a:

> Multiply the gap by **2** repeatedly, etc.

The next number will be: **62**

The sequence can be explained as a Double Operation:

3b. Double Operations
(Two operations, e.g. multiply, then subtract for the next number)

$(\times 2 + 2)$, $(\times 2 + 2)$, $(\times 2 + 2)$, $(\times 2 + 2)$, $(\times 2 + 2)$

0, 2, 6, 14, 30, ?

Example 3b:

> Multiply by **2**, then add **2**, etc.

The next number will be: **62**

Exercise 6: 4   Find the missing number:

Score

1) **2, 4, 8, 16, _____**

2) **100,000, 10,000, 1,000, 100, _____**

3) **2, 20, 200, 2,000, _____**

4) **0, 10, 30, 70, _____**

5) **3, 4, 6, 10, _____**

6) **60,000, 6,000, 600, 60,** _____

7) **3, 8, 18, 33,** _____

8) **18, 15, 22, 19, 26,** _____

9) **20, 12, 8, 6,** _____

10) **5, 10, 30, 120,** _____

c. Mixed Examples

Exercise 6: 5   Find the missing number:

Score

1) **20, 18, 16, 14, 12,** _____

2) **7, 10, 13, 16, 19,** _____

3) **2, 2, 3, 5, 8,** _____

4) **3, 6, 9, 12, 15,** _____

5) **3, 7, 9, 13, 15,** _____

6) **32, 27, 22, 17, 12,** _____

7) **89, 91, 93, 95, 97,** _____

8) **101, 96, 91, 86, 81,** _____

9) **2, 4, 12, 48,** _____

10) **3, 30, 300, 3,000,** _____

4. Number Links

The Four Rules of Number are the basis for all **Number Link** questions: $+ \; - \; \times \; \div$
There are two types of number link question:

Single Operation • **Double Operation**

a. Single Operation

Single Operation number link questions involve performing one mathematical calculation. $(+ - \times \div)$

Example:

Find the missing number:

(13 [39] 3)   **(14 [56] 4)**
(15 [?] 5)

Identify the operation; multiply in this example.
Multiply **15** $\times$ **5 = 75**

$\overset{\times}{\frown}$
(13 [39] 3)   **(14 [56] 4)**

$\overset{\times}{\frown}$
(15 [75] 5)

Exercise 6: 6a Find the missing number:

Score

1) **(1 [5] 4)**   **(6 [9] 3)**
    (8 [?] 10)   _____

2) **(10 [8] 2)**   **(7 [3] 4)**
    (9 [?] 3)   _____

3) **(2 [6] 3)**   **(5 [10] 2)**
    (4 [?] 5)   _____

4) (7 [10] 3)   (15 [17] 2)
  (3 [?] 14)   _____

5) (10 [5] 2)   (30 [3] 10)
  (6 [?] 2)   _____

b. Double Operations

Double Operation number link questions involve performing two mathematical calculations (+ − × ÷) to produce the linking third number.

1. Type 1 - Linear Calculations

Example: | Find the missing number:
(4 [8] 16)   (5 [10] 20)
  (6 [?] 24)

Identify the operation that is used twice in this example.

$$\overset{\times 2}{\frown}\,\overset{\times 2}{\frown}$$ (4 [8] 16) $$\overset{\times 2}{\frown}\,\overset{\times 2}{\frown}$$ (5 [10] 20)

Multiply 6 × 2 = 12 × 2 = 24 $$\overset{\times 2}{\frown}\,\overset{\times 2}{\frown}$$ (6 [12] 24)

Exercise 6: 6b Find the missing number:

6) (19 [14] 9)   (15 [10] 5)
  (11 [?] 1)   _____

7) (27 [9] 3)   (18 [6] 2)
  (36 [?] 4)   _____

8) **(7 [15] 23)**   **(14 [22] 30)**

         (21 [?] 37)   _____

9) **(4 [16] 64)**   **(3 [12] 48)**

         (5 [?] 80)   _____

10) **(40 [29] 18)**   **(32 [21] 10)**

         (25 [?] 3)   _____

5. Mixed Examples

Exercise 6: 7   Answer the following:

Score

1) a) **A = 1, B = 2, C = 3, D = 4, E = 5**
What is the answer to this sum written as a letter?

   B + C = _____

   b) **A = 2, B = 3, C = 4, D = 6, E = 8**
What is the answer to this sum written as a letter?

   E ÷ A = _____

2) a) **A = 1, B = 5, C = 6, D = 8, E = 10**
What is the answer to this sum written as a letter?

   E ÷ B + C = _____

b) **A = 0, B = 1, C = 2, D = 4, E = 8**
What is the answer to this sum written as a letter?

B × E − D = _____

3) a) **A = 1, B = 2, C = 3, D = 4, E = 5**
What is the answer to this sum written as a letter?

D ÷ B × C − A = _____

b) **A = 0, B = 1, C = 2, D = 4, E = 8**
What is the answer to this sum written as a letter?

C × D ÷ B + A = _____

---

4) a) **3 × 5 = 5 × [?]** _____

b) **28 ÷ 4 = 8 − [?]** _____

c) **17 + 17 = 19 + [?]** _____

5) a) **11 × 6 = 78 − [?]** _____

b) **29 + 8 = 18 + [?]** _____

c) **5 × 12 = 10 × [?]** _____

6) a) **4 × 16 = 8 × [?]** _____

b) **18 ÷ 2 = 6 + [?]** _____

c) **56 ÷ 7 = 64 ÷ [?]** _____

7) a) **20,   18,   14,   8,** _____

   b) **3,   6,   12,   24,** _____

   c) **1,   3,   9,   27,** _____

8) a) **2,   13,   4,   11,   6,   9,** _____

   b) **4,   8,   16,   32,** _____

   c) **416,   208,   104,   52,   26,** _____

---

9) a) **(16 [4] 1)   (32 [8] 2)**

   (48 [?] 3)   _____

   b) **(14 [35] 21)   (8 [34] 26)**

   (15 [?] 12)   _____

   c) **(40 [8] 5)   (30 [5] 6)**

   (60 [?] 6)   _____

10) a) **(9 [36] 4)   (8 [56] 7)**

   (9 [?] 9)   _____

   b) **(23 [32] 41)   (19 [28] 37)**

   (16 [?] 34)   _____

   c) **(41 [25] 16)   (29 [16] 13)**

   (36 [?] 17)   _____

Chapter Seven
REVISION

1. Letter Sequencing

A B C D E F G H I J K L M N O P Q R S T U V W X Y Z

Exercise 7: 1a Write the missing letters:

1) LC   ME   NG   OI   _____

2) FH   HJ   JL   LN   _____

3) XV   ZU   BT   DS   _____

4) MJ   PG   SD   VA   _____

5) TU   UV   VW   WX   XY   YZ   _____

2. Alphabet Codes

Exercise 7: 1b Write the missing letters:

6) **FD** is to **HA** as **WJ** is to **?** _____

7) **GJ** is to **KH** as **PS** is to **?** _____

8) If the code for **FAR** is **DYP**, what is the code for **SEA**? _____

9) If the code for **MAT** is **NCW**, what does **SWJ** stand for? _____

10) If the code for **RAN** is **IZM**, what is the code for **JOG**? _____

Score

3. One Word Patterns

Exercise 7: 2a Fill in the missing word:

1) (**swot   tows**)   (**liar   rail**)
    (**flog   ?**)   _____

2) (**faint   fit**)   (**chain   can**)
    (**scoop   ?**)   _____

3) (**deaf   fade**)   (**ream   mare**)
    (**inks   ?**)   _____

4) (**crews   screw**)   (**hooks   shook**)
    (**kills   ?**)   _____

5) (**denim   mined**)   (**lived   devil**)
    (**stink   ?**)   _____

4. Two Word Patterns

Exercise 7: 2b Fill in the missing word:

6) (**risk [skid] idol**)   (**lisp [_____] item**)

7) (**sham [shod] clod**)   (**stop [_____] whet**)

8) (**gloat [lop] pinch**)   (**shoes [_____] tenet**)

9) (**round [dear] heard**)   (**dwarf [_____] horns**)

10) (**duets [flue] flags**)   (**marsh [_____] scalp**)

5. Secret Codes

Exercise 7: 3a Find the answers to the following:

Match these number codes to the correct words:

TRUE	EATS	TONE	REAR
4672	3253	4312	2548

1) Find the code for the word **NEST**. _____

2) What word has the code **3542**? _____

3) Find the code for the word **SOAR**. _____

Match these number codes to the correct words:

HEAD	OVER	VEER	DOME
8994	7569	3917	

4) Find the code for the word **MADE**. _____

5) What word has the code **4516**? _____

6. Letter Shifts

Exercise 7: 3b Move a letter from the first word to the second word to make two new words:

6) **FIEND** and **TAP**   become _____ and _____

7) **STASH** and **SIR**   become _____ and _____

8) **MORON** and **PATS**   become _____ and _____

9) **THANK** and **SEAR**   become _____ and _____

10) **SCRUM** and **BOOM**   become _____ and _____

7. Compound Words

Exercise 7: 4a Write the compound word:

1) **(any many now)**
   (day works thing)

   _____

2) **(birthday pan sponge)**
   (biscuit party cake)

   _____

3) **(numb cold frost)**
   (snow bite winter)

   _____

4) **(page text exercise)**
   (book writing paper)

   _____

5) **(rat mice cat)**
   (mouse her trap)

   _____

8. Hidden Words

Exercise 7: 4b Find the four-letter word hidden in the sentence:

6) A visa has a date stamp. _____

7) You shouldn't tell one another's secrets. _____

8) Steven's building plans were much altered. _____

9) Tina had to admit she'd cheated. _____

10) The bottles shook in the crate. _____

Score

9. Missing Letters

Exercise 7: 5a Fill in the missing letter:

1) **mov** [?] **mu**
   rat [?] **ven**

   The letter is ____ .

2) **per** [?] **erb**
   sin [?] **ing**

   The letter is ____ .

3) **ra** [?] **ain**
   son [?] **ive**

   The letter is ____ .

4) **len** [?] **im**
   mai [?] **ial**

   The letter is ____ .

5) **sol** [?] **nto**
   to [?] **tter**

   The letter is ____ .

10. Analogies

Exercise 7: 5b Underline the word that will complete the analogy:

6) **Note** is to **singer** as **word** is to (writer, page, letter)

7) **Fish** is to **gills** as **mammal** is to (lungs, air, breathe)

8) **Poet** is to **poem** as **author** is to (character, write, story)

9) **Stem** is to **flower** as **trunk** is to (bush, seed, tree)

10) **Jog** is to **run** as **hop** is to (jump, bounce, fall)

Score

11. Similar Meanings

Exercise 7: 6a
Underline the two words that are most similar in meaning:

1) (area   street   farm)   (district   house   firm)

2) (hat   fury   pain)   (stroke   blow   rage)

3) (slow   move   active)   (dead   lively   jumpy)

4) (dog   safe   protect)   (wall   prison   guard)

5) (profit   money   manager)   (gain   bank   rate)

12. Word Links

Exercise 7: 6b
Underline one word that links with both pairs of words:

6) (puny   feeble)   (unfit   unhealthy)

   (ill, old, weak, strong, useless)

7) (myth   fable)   (cotton   wool)

   (story, truth, tale, yarn, character)

8) (hole   crack)   (break   interval)

   (vacant, empty, gap, cut, smash)

9) (lean   thin)   (agile   strong)

   (cable, skinny, spare, wiry, stocky)

10) (house   flat)   (palace   mansion)

   (castle, build, dwelling, land, caravan)

Score

13. Opposite Meanings

Exercise 7: 7a
Write the words most opposite in meaning:

1) (wise silly knowledge)
   (advice clever foolish)

   _____ _____

2) (camp host hotel)
   (holiday stay guest)

   _____ _____

3) (king English lesson)
   (school subject country)

   _____ _____

4) (judge guilty plead)
   (innocent court law)

   _____ _____

5) (memory mind remember)
   (lose forget omit)

   _____ _____

14. Odd Ones Out

Exercise 7: 7b
Write the two odd ones out:

6) cabbage, carrot, pine,
   lilac, turnip

   _____ _____

7) weep, yell, wail,
   bite, cry

   _____ _____

8) peace, noise, calm,
   rest, worry

   _____ _____

9) iron, copper, marble,
   zinc, stone

   _____ _____

10) thrush, falcon, eagle,
    vulture, robin

   _____ _____

Score

15. Missing Words

Exercise 7: 8a What is the missing three-letter word?

1) The orchestra **PERMED** in the school.

   The five possibilities are:
   ALL NOT FOR FAR FEE   _____

2) Workmen should be paid for their **LAB**.

   The five possibilities are:
   ATE OUR LOW ARE ONE   _____

3) Our holiday destination was **SHERN** Italy.

   The five possibilities are:
   OWN OUT TOO AIL LOW   _____

4) After the war the countries wanted **CE**.

   The five possibilities are:
   DIE PIE PEE PEA LEA   _____

5) There was a **PUP** show on the beach.

   The five possibilities are:
   PAT PET PUT POT PIT   _____

16. Logical Reasoning

Exercise 7: 8b Answer the following:

6) Davina, James and Simon play hockey. Robert plays basketball, cricket and hockey. Naomi plays cricket but does not play hockey. All the children except Davina and Simon play football. James plays basketball.

   (Clue: draw a table to help you)

   a) Who plays every sport?   _____

   b) Which children only play one sport? _____ _____

   c) Which child plays two sports?   _____

7) Some children were comparing their birth dates. Norris is older than Larry but not as old as Patricia. Tony was younger than Patricia but older than Norris. Carla found she was the youngest.

a) Who was in the middle in terms of age? _____

b) Who was the oldest? _____

8) ***A book has a number of pages. The pages are made of paper.***

Underline the only statement which must be True.

Books are completely made of paper.
All books have hundreds of pages.
Books are full of pages made from paper.
Paper is only used to make books.

9) Timothy is facing south. He turns clockwise one full turn and another half turn. Which way is Timothy facing now. _____

A. North
B. West
C. South
D. East

10) Yesterday was Friday. What day will it be two days after tomorow? _____

A. Monday
B. Tuesday
C. Thursday
D. Wednesday

Score

17. Substitution

Exercise 7: 9a Write the answer as a letter:

1) $A = 2, B = 3, C = 5, D = 8, E = 12$
What is the answer to this sum written as a letter?

$$D - B = \underline{\hspace{2cm}}$$

2) $A = 4, B = 6, C = 8, D = 10, E = 12$
What is the answer to this sum written as a letter?

$$E \div B + C = \underline{\hspace{2cm}}$$

3) $A = 4, B = 8, C = 16, D = 32, E = 64$
What is the answer to this sum written as a letter?

$$E \div C + A = \underline{\hspace{2cm}}$$

4) $A = 3, B = 10, C = 15, D = 20, E = 30$
What is the answer to this sum written as a letter?

$$D + C + B \div C = \underline{\hspace{2cm}}$$

5) $A = 1, B = 2, C = 5, D = 6, E = 10$
What is the answer to this sum written as a letter?

$$A \times B \times C \div E = \underline{\hspace{2cm}}$$

18. Arithmetic Equations

Exercise 7: 9b Find the missing number:

6) $2 \times 4 = 4 \times [?]$ $\underline{\hspace{1.5cm}}$

7) $15 \times 3 = 5 \times [?]$ $\underline{\hspace{1.5cm}}$

8) $42 \div 7 = 18 \div [?]$ $\underline{\hspace{1.5cm}}$

9) $12 + 18 = 55 - [?]$ $\underline{\hspace{1.5cm}}$

10) $19 - 7 = 48 \div [?]$ $\underline{\hspace{1.5cm}}$

Score

19. Number Sequencing

Exercise 7: 10a   Find the missing number:

Score

1) **1, 2, 4, 7, 11,** _____

2) **3, 6, 12, 24,** _____

3) **31, 30, 27, 22, 15,** _____

4) **15, 18, 12, 15, 9,** _____

5) **5, 10, 20, 35, 55,** _____

20. Number Links

Exercise 7: 10b   Find the missing number:

6) **(40 [5] 8)   (60 [10] 6)**
   (80 [?] 16) _____

7) **(21 [13] 5)   (32 [24] 16)**
   (25 [?] 9) _____

8) **(9 [20] 11)   (16 [30] 14)**
   (22 [?] 18) _____

9) **(14 [56] 4)   (15 [60] 4)**
   (13 [?] 4) _____

10) **(2 [6] 18)   (4 [12] 36)**
   (5 [?] 45) _____

Answers

Chapter Five
Logical Reasoning

Exercise 5: 1a

1) a) Xu-min
   b) Alex
2) a) Louise
   b) Michael
3) a) Ruth
   b) Rupa
4) A. Ray and Jasper

Exercise 5: 1b

5) A. False
   B. Unknown
   C. True
6) A. False
   B. False
   C. True
7) A. Unknown
   B. False
   C. False

Exercise 5: 1c

8) a) A. Unknown
      B. True
      C. Unknown
   b) A. True
      B. Unknown
      C. False

Exercise 5: 1d

9) a) London is an English city.
   b) Oranges grow on citrus fruit trees.
10) a) Pandas are black and white bears.
    b) Crocodiles attack their prey from the water.

Exercise 5: 2a

1) A. True
   B. False
   C. Unknown
2) A. False
   B. Unknown
   C. True
3) A. False
   B. False
   C. True
4) A. False
   B. False
   C. Unknown

Exercise 5: 2b

5) a) C. Cameron is 12
   b) Tuesday

Exercise 5: 2c

6) A. False
   B. Unknown
   C. False
   D. True
7) a) Some books contain facts.
   b) Moats surround many castle fortresses.
8) C. Deborah took 48 seconds to run the race.
9) D. Twelve years old
10) a) C. Monday
    b) C. The 29th of September

Chapter Six
Mathematical Reasoning

Exercise 6: 1

1) D
2) A
3) D
4) B
5) A

Answers

6) E
7) D
8) D
9) D
10) C

Exercise 6: 2
1) 1
2) 5
3) 2
4) 10
5) 3
6) 3
7) 6
8) 4
9) 1
10) 20

Exercise 6: 3
1) 5
2) 3
3) 31
4) 17
5) 5
6) 17
7) 16
8) 13
9) 5
10) 5

Exercise 6: 4
1) 32
2) 10
3) 20,000
4) 150
5) 18
6) 6
7) 53

8) 23
9) 5
10) 600

Exercise 6: 5
1) 10
2) 22
3) 12
4) 18
5) 19
6) 7
7) 99
8) 76
9) 240
10) 30,000

Exercise 6: 6a
1) 18
2) 6
3) 20
4) 17
5) 3

Exercise 6: 6b
6) 6
7) 12
8) 29
9) 20
10) 14

Exercise 6: 7
1) a) E
   b) C
2) a) D
   b) D
3) a) E
   b) E
4) a) 3
   b) 1
   c) 15

Answers

5) a) 12
   b) 19
   c) 6
6) a) 8
   b) 3
   c) 8
7) a) 0
   b) 48
   c) 81
8) a) 8
   b) 64
   c) 13
9) a) 12
   b) 27
   c) 10
10) a) 81
   b) 25
   c) 19

Chapter Seven
Revision

Exercise 7: 1a
1) PK
2) NP
3) FR
4) YX
5) ZA

Exercise 7: 1b
6) YG
7) TQ
8) QCY
9) RUG
10) QLT

Exercise 7: 2a
1) golf
2) sop
3) skin
4) skill
5) knits

Exercise 7: 2b
6) spit
7) stet
8) hot
9) ford
10) scar

Exercise 7: 3a
1) 7284
2) RATE
3) 8653
4) 6179
5) ROAM

Exercise 7: 3b
6) find and tape (e)
7) sash and stir (t)
8) moon and parts (r)
9) tank and shear (h)
10) scum and broom (r)

Exercise 7: 4a
1) anything
2) pancake
3) frostbite
4) textbook
5) rather

Exercise 7: 4b
6) test
7) lone
8) halt
9) toad
10) less

Exercise 7: 5a
1) e
2) k
3) g
4) d
5) o

Answers

Exercise 7: 5b
6) writer
7) lungs
8) story
9) tree
10) jump

Exercise 7: 6a
1) area, district
2) fury, rage
3) active, lively
4) protect, guard
5) profit, gain

Exercise 7: 6b
6) weak
7) yarn
8) gap
9) wiry
10) dwelling

Exercise 7: 7a
1) wise, foolish
2) host, guest
3) king, subject
4) guilty, innocent
5) remember, forget

Exercise 7: 7b
6) pine & lilac
7) yell & bite
8) noise & worry
9) marble & stone
10) thrush & robin

Exercise 7: 8a
1) FOR
2) OUR
3) OUT
4) PEA
5) PET

Exercise 7: 8b
6) a) Robert
   b) Davina and Simon
   c) Naomi
7) a) Norris
   b) Patricia
8) Books are full of pages
   made from paper.
9) A. North
10) B. Tuesday

Exercise 7: 9a
1) C
2) D
3) B
4) A
5) A

Exercise 7: 9b
6) 2
7) 9
8) 3
9) 25
10) 4

Exercise 7: 10a
1) 16
2) 48
3) 6
4) 12
5) 80

Exercise 7: 10b
6) 5
7) 17
8) 40
9) 52
10) 15

PROGRESS CHARTS

Shade in your score for each exercise on the graph. Add up for your total score. An adult will work out the percentage.

5. LOGICAL REASONING

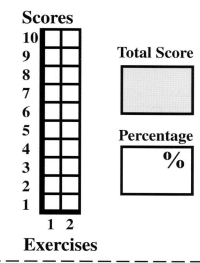

6. MATHEMATICAL REASONING

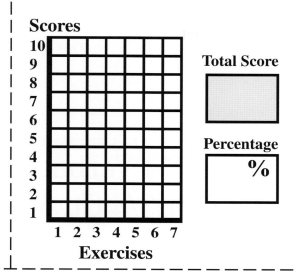

7. REVISION

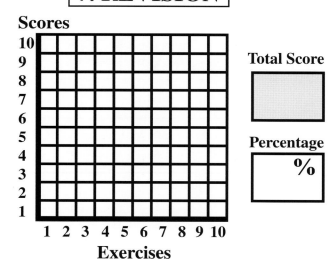

Add up the percentages and divide by 3

Overall Percentage

%

CERTIFICATE OF

ACHIEVEMENT

This certifies

_____

has successfully completed

11+ Verbal Reasoning
Year 3/4 GL & Other Styles
WORKBOOK **2**

Overall percentage
score achieved **%**

Comment _____

_____

Signed _____
(teacher/parent/guardian)

Date _____